ℛℛ
RAVETTE PUBLISHING

© Bamforth and Company Limited 2013
Licensed by JELC Ltd
All rights reserved.

First published in 2013 by
Ravette Publishing Limited
PO Box 876, Horsham
West Sussex RH12 9GH

ISBN: 978-1-84161-368-0

HOW TO BEAT THE
BREATHALYSER

**NO DRIVING LICENCE
REQUIRED
NO BREATHALYSER TEST
TO BE FEARED
CHEAP TO RUN.....AND...
ALL THE DRINK YOU
WANT ON TAP !!**

"WHAT HAPPENED BERT, DID YOU MISS A STEP?"
"NO — **I HIT EVERY RUDDY ONE!!**"

A 'BAMFORTH' COMIC

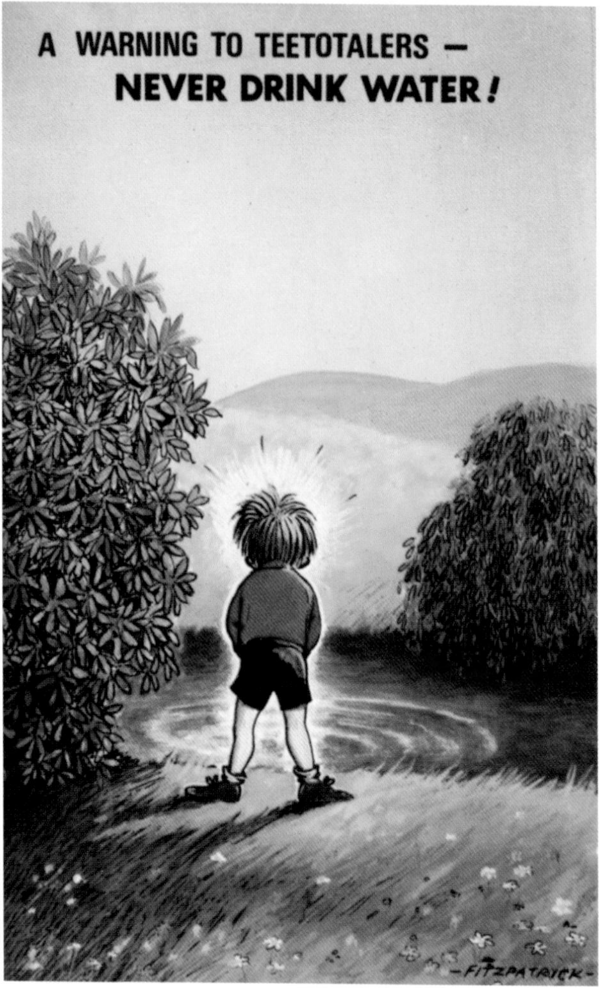
A WARNING TO TEETOTALERS –
NEVER DRINK WATER!
-FITZPATRICK-

" HASH BERT BEEN IN TONIGHT LOVE ? "
" YES ABOUT AN HOUR AGO."
" WAS I WITH HIM ? "

Other titles available in this series ...

	ISBN	Price
Love Will Find a Way	978-1-84161-367-3	£5.99

HOW TO ORDER:

Please send a cheque/postal order in £ sterling, made payable to
'Ravette Publishing' for the cover price of the book/s and allow the
following for post & packing ...

UK & BFPO	70p for the first book & 40p per book thereafter
Europe & Eire	£1.30 for the first book & 70p per book thereafter
Rest of the world	£2.20 for the first book & £1.10 per book thereafter

RAVETTE PUBLISHING LTD
PO Box 876, Horsham, West Sussex   RH12 9GH
Tel: 01403 711443   Fax: 01403 711554   Email: ingrid@ravettepub.co.uk

Prices and availability are subject to change without prior notice